Griggs Anthology

Daylight Song

Writing Contest Winners
Across the River
East Bay Writers' Roundtable

MANFIT PRESS

San Ramon, California

Library of Congress Cataloging-in-Publication Data

Daylight song : Griggs anthology.
       p.   cm.
   "Selections originally presented at the annual writing contest of the 'Across the River' East Bay Writers' Roundtable."--T.p. verso.
   ISBN 0-922530-04-1   (alk. paper) $11.00
   1. American literature--California--San Francisco Bay Area.
2. San Francisco Bay Area (Calif.)--Literary collections.
3. American literature--20th century. I. "Across the River" East Bay Writers' Roundtable. II. Griggs anthology.
PS572.S33D39   1996
810.8 ' 07946--dc20   95-53037
                                                                        CIP

Publisher: Rick Griggs, Manfit Press
Editing: Fred Norman
Printing: Thomson-Shore
Printed in the United States of America

10 9 8 7 6 5 4 3 2 1

You may order this book from your bookstore. This title may also be purchased from the publisher in quantity discounts.

For more information on the East Bay Writers' Roundtable or the annual writing contest write or call:

MANFIT Press
Attn. EBWR
P.O. Box 2390
San Ramon, CA 94583
510/866-0793

Cover design by Lila Aminian
Cover illustration by Robin Bomberry

Acknowledgments
Daylight Song

There are four members of the Writers' Roundtable who willingly tackled major parts of our group's efforts. *Thank You,* Blanche Abrams, for competently managing the monthly meetings and the quarterly "Evenings of Literary Enjoyment." *Merci Beaucoup,* Fred Norman, for coordinating contest judging and editing the annual anthology. *Danke Shöne,* Steve Hellman, for your editorial coaching, contest judging, and leadership with the quarterly readings. Finally, a big *Gracias,* to Mary Lou Slater for your support and industry contacts that make this publication financially possible.

This venture survives thanks to the love and devotion of those who attend the meetings, cook food, set-up, clean-up, read their work, and gently critique other works. A special thanks goes to Agnes Assada, Heike Beinling, and Isabel Gonzalez for assistance in translating the International Page. A large portion of our existence is based on sales of the book you are holding. We thank you for the support. All of the proceeds are used for publication, postage, copying, etc. We appreciate our members who dutifully purchase their two copies each year. We are grateful to all of you who pick up a copy for yourself and maybe a gift copy for someone who loves reading, writing, and a good cause.

Major Sponsors

Book Design:
Lila Aminian
California Design Group
San Jose, California

Cover, Endsheets:
Mary Lou Slater
Holliston Mills
San Ramon, California
Kingsport, Tennessee

Book Printing:
Jim Holefka
Thomson-Shore, Inc.
Quality Book Manufacturing
Dexter, Michigan

Shipping:
Margaret Clifton
California Western Freight
Yuba City, California

Dust Jacket:
Color Dot, Inc.
Maryland Heights, Missouri

From The Publisher

The phone rings and a teenage voice asks, "I heard about a writing contest—Is this the place where I can send my poems?" I say, "It certainly is; how did you hear about it? . . . good luck!"

     The mail comes in and under the stack, there is one large brown envelope. It's addressed to Manfit Press, Writing Contest, with a return address:

          Newcastle near GREYSTONES
          Co. Wicklow, Republic of Ireland

It is our first international entry! I'm beginning to believe that our Writers' Roundtable Contest is shaping up quite nicely. It's a thrill to present the second collection of short stories, poems, and non-fiction works from winning poets and authors.

Each month we hold our meetings, and each quarter we offer to the public "An Evening of Literary Enjoyment" where readers present their original works. During it all, we sometimes wonder if and when we will have the new Anthology. Here it is! And we hope you will enjoy it.

I treasure the images of contest entrants walking up to the stage, collecting their certificate, receiving their cash prize, and knowing they will be published. On the other end, I know we've done well when a reader looks up from the anthology and says, "Oh my! That piece was beautiful. Where do you find these good writers?" I used to say, "They're in my living room each month." Maybe after the next contest, I'll have to say that we find them all over the world. And that's as it should be.

Rick Griggs
San Ramon, California

Daylight Song Contents

More Winners

. . . *And More Winners*

Golden Child

Charlene Villella

Each dawn I am drawn to your room,
from the doorway I watch you, I know that
outside the sun rises to drizzle gold down
a palette of clouds as it paints a new day
Then glides across the water, rides the breeze
up the shale cliffs, peeks into caves and
drinks dew off purple ice plant

It runs across the meadow, pulls songs from birds,
Rides dust motes into your bed then licks its way
up from your chin to touch your eyes,
highlights your night-tossed hair

You wake, a smile tugs the corners of your mouth
You stretch out your arms, try to catch the light
giggling as it trickles between your fingers
beginning each day bathed in golden light the only
thing that reaches into your autistic world,
that you don't ignore

Someday,
will you reach for me
the way you do the sun

Brother Wheaton's Trip Abroad

Cissi Shannon

It was during revival time — a long week of services at the church both morning and evening. Mama was frantically busy every waking minute. The visiting preacher stayed with us at the parsonage, and Mama was the most hospitable of hostesses; the visiting preacher had his every wish fulfilled, usually before he realized he wanted anything. Besides keeping her extrasensory perception at its keenest, Mama also had to see that the flowers in the church were not only fresh, but were arranged to her satisfaction. She must take the time to run her finger over the pews to check for dust. And she insisted on getting to every service early enough to personally greet each worshipper appropriately — a handshake, a pat on the back, or, in the case of men and boys she particularly liked, a resounding thump on the biceps. Many winced through their smiles when being welcomed by Mama. But they considered her a town character and they loved her, accepting her rather painful greetings in the spirit in which they were given. All this, plus her regular tasks of mothering and housework, took more than all of Mama's time.

Daddy was very busy during revival time, too. There was his duty as host to the visiting evangelist, and there was also his moral obligation to look after the visiting singer. While the evangelist was always an established shepherd of his own flock in another town, the singers were usually upstart, aspiring preachers, ministerial students from Mississippi College, and Daddy felt tremendous responsibility for them. In his rather bigoted opinion, their hormones were significantly out-of-balance because of their youth, and the young women and girls of Huddleston needed protection from their charms. Also attributable to their youth was the fact that these young men, despite their charisma, had no real common sense. They might oversleep and be late for morning services; or they might not remember which of the ladies of the church had loaded her table with fried chicken and speckled butter beans for their nourishment. They might also do great harm by getting into political discussion with some of the townsfolk or expressing their opinions on social concerns. In Daddy's mind, the primary task for revival week was the salvation of souls, and he, as pastor of the church, wanted no time wasted on trivia.

The ladies of the congregation had long since thrown up their hands at the prospect of inviting our whole family to meals during revival time. Only Mama and Daddy were invited to their homes with the visitors twice a day. Not that there wasn't enough food: We often wondered how the clergy managed to keep a service going for two or more hours after having eaten an enormous dinner and a supper of chicken, ham and pork chops, three kinds of beans, at least one mess of greens, four potato dishes, rice and gravy, hot biscuits and cornbread, and several different salads smeared with homemade mayonnaise. This would be followed by offerings of various cakes, pies and cookies, or more hot biscuits soaked in warm, sweetened blackberries and topped with fresh whipped cream. But the ladies had learned from bitter experience that their pastor's children caused trouble, leading their own offspring into unbecoming mischief, causing the ladies embarrassment in the face of their dignified guests.

This Sunday we were sent home from the morning services with instructions to stay there until Mama arrived. Daddy and the guest clergy would spend the time between dinner and supper visiting church members who had not attended the revival services (heaping coals of fire on their heads), or planning strategy for salvation of souls at the evening service.

We children arrived home, downed our banana-and-pineapple salad and cheese toast, and were wiping our milk mustaches when discussion turned to how the hot summer afternoon should be spent. This was the last day of the revival, and both our parents would likely be with the visitors for most of the afternoon. Cathy mentioned that Brother Wheaton, the evangelist, would be leaving tonight for a trip to somewhere in Europe to attend a meeting of the Baptist World Alliance.

"I cain't stand the way Brother Wheaton tawks," said Ruchelle, "So highfalutin'. Here's how he prays." She stood tall, her small belly extended to simulate his portliness, swaying slightly on the balls of her feet, raising her arm above her head, her voice as sonorous as a twelve-year-old girl could muster, "Ah-wer haay-ven-lee faahh-thaah." In high glee, we took turns imitating Brother Wheaton's very affected salutation to God. Then someone said, "We haven't done much to him, except tyin' his chair to the table leg the other mornin'," followed by another comment, "He sure looks mean with that double lip and those big ol' horn-rim glasses."

"He sure does. If we did much more to him, no tellin' what he'd do," I said. Being the youngest, I hadn't been involved in most of the activities of my sisters in previous years when we had visiting preachers.

"Well," Cathy's dark eyes danced from one sister to the next, "What *could* he do — if he's halfway 'round the world when he finds out?"

"Naw, yawl!" exclaimed Francine, whose nervous mama had sent her home with us after church. Francine's mama was serving the preachers their Sunday dinner, and Francine was a child who constantly annoyed her mother in one way or another. "Yo' mama said we's to behave ourselves. I don't wanta get into none of yawl's trouble. Don't yawl start nothin'!"

"We ain't startin' anything. We're just tawkin'," said Ruchelle, rather enjoying Francine's discomfort. "But it sure would be fun. Yawl remember the funny look on Brother Gilbert's face last year, after we'd put the perfume on his clean underwear? Brother Sullivan thought it was funny when he found the lace on his BVD's that time, but Brother Gilbert didn't say anything — just kep' on giving us them funny looks!" She chortled at the memory.

"Who was the one with fat hands and skinny feet? He couldn't get the newspaper outa his shoes 'cause the tacks in the paper kep' on stickin' his fingers! He was late to church — had to run all the way to make it when he did! He was still a-puffin' when he got to the pulpit!" We giggled delightedly at our particular impressions of the tardy, fat-handed preacher gasping for breath during his invocation.

"Well, I'm real sorry Brother Wheaton's leavin' tonight," Gin spoke in mock sadness. "We shoulda short-sheeted him, at least. He prob'ly has trouble sleepin' anyway, with that fat lip hangin' in his mouth." At this prospect, we broke into howls of laughter. "Wonder if he snores?" Cathy, her whole body a-quiver with giggles, made long, loud snoring noises, gasping and coughing. Our laughter grew louder and brighter. "He's so ugly! How you think he'd look with lace on the *outside* his clothes!" The giggles and chortles mounted to guffaws.

Cathy ran from the table and returned with mama's sewing basket. "Look-a here," she said, her hands rummaging the contents, "This is the lef'-over lace from your new dress, Sissy Baby." I sniffed importantly. "The lace will never come off that dress," I declared. "Mama showed me the lock-stitch she used to put it on." Nobody seemed interested in hearing about Mama's new sewing technique.

"Looka this gold braid!" Cathy's hands were still busy with the basket. "We could make his suit look like a band uniform!" Mental pictures of a spangled and feathered Brother Wheaton marching in step, his heavy upper lip wrapped around the mouthpiece of a glinting trombone sent us into shrieks of joy, which gradually dwindled into thoughtful silence. Then Gin's authoritative voice, "Let's go," she ordered, "Mama could be back 'fore long."

When Mama returned later in the afternoon and found us sprawled on the living room floor reading the Sunday funnies, she smiled on us fondly, saying how nice it was to see us spending the Lord's day quietly and not causing any trouble. She was so proud of us all, she said. Humming "Tell It To Jesus" she disappeared into her bedroom to take off her hat and readjust the bun at the nape of her neck. "What's the sewing basket doing out, girls?" she called. Her voice was light and held no great demand for an honest answer. "Uh, Francine ripped her hem," replied Ruchelle, by far the most accomplished liar, "But we got it fixed OK." We hardly breathed until Mama picked up her tune again, "You- have-a no uh-ther- sucha- friend or bruh-ther.."

Brother Wheaton's wife came for the final service, arriving at our house about an hour before church started. Although Mrs. Wheaton dramatically claimed exhaustion from her thirty-mile drive, all alone, from her house to ours, she would take her husband to the airport in Jackson immediately after he finished preaching. Sounding very important, Brother Wheaton warned Daddy that the invitation hymn must be cut short to allow his prompt departure, and he solemnly accounted to his wife that he had done all his packing before the morning service. His plan, he said proudly, was to change from his white duck preaching suit into his dark traveling suit at the airport. He calculated he would have just enough time to make the change. He then gathered his luggage and very carefully stowed it in the trunk of Mrs. Wheaton's car.

A few weeks later Daddy stepped firmly to the dinner table, having just come from the post office. There was a letter in his hand. "Girls," he said gravely, holding the folded letter up for us to see, "I will read this to you — then I'd like to hear your comments." He took his usual place at the head of the table, unfolded the letter, gazed at each of us in turn, cleared his throat thoughtfully, and read:

Dear Brother Wilson:
I wish to thank you for the opportunity given me to preach in the name of the Lord to your fine congregation and visitors. I am presently in Brussels, and am enjoying meeting good Baptist people from all parts of the world. I do feel you should know, however, that I encountered some difficulty in getting to this meeting.

At this point, Daddy looked from one to another of us. There was considerable squirming on the hard seats of the dining room chairs. He continued,

Upon my arrival at the airport in Jackson, I carried my bag into the men's room, took my traveling suit from it, removed my white suit and put it into the bag, which I then gave to a porter to check through for me, because time was short. Hurriedly attempting to put on my traveling suit, I found that I could not get my arms into the coat. The sleeves were sewed closed at both the upper arm and wrist openings. The trousers had also been sewed closed, at the fly, as well as at the ankles. I must congratulate Mrs. Wilson for teaching your daughters to make firm and strong stitches. Every stitch had to be cut separately. In fact, I could not remove the gold braid on the shoulders and lapels. It had to remain in place throughout my trip, which caused me a great deal of embarrassment, particularly in the New York airport, where a number of rude young heathens — military men — kept referring to me as 'the brass.'

There was a sound like a sob from Mama's end of the table, but nobody seemed to be crying — yet. Mama's eyes were fixed on Daddy and I couldn't interpret her expression. After another hard look at each of us, Daddy returned to the letter.

The plane came in and the other passengers boarded. Then they began to call for me over the loudspeaker. I was still trying desperately to get into my suit. Mrs. Wheaton became frantic because I had not come out of the men's room and, of course, it would have been improper for her to enter. She finally sent the porter, who saw my distressful position and, after giving me his pocket knife to cut the stitches, rushed out to ask that the plane be held for me. My only fortune in the entire situation was that the pilot was considerate and waited for me to board.

Daddy paused in reading. I peeked down the table at Mama. She looked neither left nor right, but straight at Daddy, her chin in one hand, the fingers pushing her lips into a pucker. Daddy looked back at the letter.

Although no real harm was done, except for some small snags in my suit and Mrs. Wheaton's extreme agitation (the porter was unable to find smelling salts for her), I feel that I must protest the behavior of your children. After my arrival in Brussells, I found lace sewed on my undershorts, lipstick on the collar of my best shirt, my shoes stuffed with newspaper and carpet tacks, and my grip reeked of Evening in Paris perfume. I was fortunate enough to locate a laundress who was able to remove the stains, the lace and the fragrance. You are aware of Mrs. Wheaton's delicate nerves. My arrival home with stains and stitches such as those to which my clothing was subjected would have been more than my wife's emotional status could endure.

I do hope you and your lovely help-mate will be able to harness the energy of your daughters so that in the future they will find more satisfaction in doing the Lord's work than in being the ambassadors of Satan. Yours very truly, Reverend Swann Wheaton.

As Daddy concluded reading this testy epistle, there was again the sob-sound from Mama's end of the table. She quickly ran through the swinging door into the kitchen. We sisters sat wide-eyed, guiltily glancing at each other and occasionally stealing a quick peek at Daddy's stern countenance. As he was re-reading the paper in his hands, the muscles around his mouth began to twitch. Suddenly he, too, pushed away from the table and followed Mama into the kitchen.

"I reckon we're in for it now, yawl," Ruchelle said ruefully. "Yeah," whispered Cathy, "We shoulda known his mouth was fat in more ways than one!" Gin stealthily slid from her chair and crept to the swinging door, flinging it open. Our parents were leaning weakly on the sink. Mama had a dishtowel to her mouth, stifling her laughter, tears rolling down her face. Daddy was blowing his nose and wiping his eyes, his face contorted in uncontrollable mirth. He turned as if to speak sharply, but the grin refused to leave his face.

"I do feel sorry for Brother Wheaton, girls," he said, and added, "Because you and his pomposity got the best of him."

Daylight Song

Valerie Nebo

The midnight sky diminishes
As it touches the pale complexion
Created by the embers of the morning sun
Stars lose their luster
As blindness steals the glimmer in the human eye
Smoky clouds stretch their phantom-like fingers
Across the rosy canvass
Creating shadows on the still lifeless world below
The land gaining light from the life giving star
That caresses the mountain tops with warm,
embracing arms
Water begins to flow its glistening repose
And tumbles to the golden lake
That whispers images of the sun
Images marred by the breath of day
And calling the birds to wake the living beasts
Rising from slumber the creatures give harmony to
the rhythm
Darting through tree or brush or water
They disturb any well-sleeping being to life
As they join in the festivities of light
A ceaseless celebration
Only giving rest when day is stolen by the dark
When the sun burns red upon the low sky
Causing the scattered clouds to blush
Then turning to darkened, thin lines
Stretching their phantom-like fingers
Across a world full of life
The stars begin to open their eyes
As the eyes of the living things
Close once again

Safety in Numbers
Lauren Hirshberg

It is said " Safety in numbers," but in our "numbers" we were far from "safe."
His words of strength and power bonded us all with a common hate.
It was time to choose a scapegoat; who would the lucky winner be?
A group practicing different beliefs posed a threat to our humanity.
It was obvious they were inferior; look at how they dressed,
As we marched in our stiff, tight uniforms; who were we trying to impress?
Hail to our leader, he promises we will win,
We'll dominate a world free of variety; <u>new</u> lives we will begin.
First, we'll throw them into camps and shave off all of their hair,
Then we'll torture them as they work, and test how much they can bare.
Later we can kill them; but what shall we do with their remains?
Well, we can throw their Jewish bones into human ovens filled with flames
Stop, you say? But we are ahead in this war.
Why ask for a reason? Why ask what we're killing for?
<u>Power</u>, is the key in life to getting ahead,
Too bad for us to reach it, we left six million dead.
"Safety in numbers." That's what they always say,
But if I faced you by myself, I would cry and run away.

The Hunter in the Rose Garden

Dennis Robertson

She stuck her head cautiously through the crevice in the rock wall. And waited without moving. Her brain and nervous system were formatted to be excellent at detecting and responding to movement. But she was at a distinct disadvantage if her adversary was still. Yet she knew they did not often stay still for long. They simply lacked the patience. Or the inclination. Yet they were formidable opponents. And she would have perished at their hands long ago had it not been for a keen awareness of them and a knowledge of their habits.

She had crossed the open space of the road to get there. This time the wooden wheels of a cart piled high with the dead had nearly run over her. It had added considerable extra time to her evening hunting to travel the additional distance to the garden. And while she knew that it was for the abundant supply of prey, part of her did not know that it was because it was simply beautiful there. And serene.

Inside the wall she scampered for the protection of the thicker bushes. She didn't stop for any push-ups or any quizzical head turning and peering with beady reptilian eyes. She had no time for that now. She had learned that she must hunt and leave quickly. For while food was plentiful, so were the humans.

Her brain contemplated while stopped. It always contemplated if it was not otherwise occupied with moving or stalking prey. Being so basic it had no choice but to function automatically. And being so primeval it held all of its history as though it were its future as well. And indeed it was. It knew, for example, or at least sensed, that she would die today. . .

A brain so ancient as hers knew its complete past, and the past of all of its race. It had a kind of pseudo memory as seen by all of its ancestors, although most were larger and fiercer than she. And of predecessors that were barely life itself, yet somehow aware. She had visions of primal plants and trees. Lush and thick. Huge. Then before that of barren landscapes and herself, or an awareness of an ancestral self, with many more legs and strangely different locomotion. She was aware of it all, yet, in the same instant, totally focused on the moment. She survived that way.

While she had remained still, a fly had been slowly moving within range. She gauged the distance carefully. And continued to wait. She had learned that it was easier to delay an attack than to miss out of impatience. Finally, the fly moved the fraction of an inch she needed, and she struck. A precisian, she was successful. She rarely missed. After all, every miss meant precious energy spent. Time wasted. Her survival depended on judgment that produced a high rate of success.

She moved carefully from bush to bush in search of a new hunting platform. All the while wary. For at any time, from any direction, she could become the prey. At this moment she could be being carefully observed. And a hunter could be watching her and waiting just as she had waited for the fly.

Even though food was more plentiful here, she had to move farther from the rock wall than usual today. And so her vulnerability increased. But the young she carried inside her required extra sustenance, and with that, extra hunting time and exposure.

A platform that almost guaranteed her success was on the other side of a small clearing. But she hesitated. A scent that was sweeter that the roses triggered caution. Without moving she surveyed the area with sight, smell and hearing. And waited. But it was getting late, her light was fading. She had little time before darkness and cold settled in; she decided to risk the extra distance from the protection of the rock wall and made a start toward. . .

"AAAHHHHH. . . ! AAAHHHHH!" The screams were terribly loud to her sensitive ears and they momentarily paralyzed her.

"A lizard! There's a lizard in my rose garden!"

In her focus on hunting, she hadn't seen the near-still figure sitting on the stone bench. She hadn't waited long enough. Instinctively she froze, perfectly unmoving. But it was the wrong instinct, and it cost her valuable time. While she froze she felt the quick beat of heavily booted feet.

"It's over there!" The shrill voice tore through her earless openings. She risked a turn of her head to identify the danger, then moved quickly toward the protection of the rock wall as the powerful feet pounded quickly toward her. Too quickly.

"I see it Your Highness! Guards! Guards!"

The lizard continued toward the wall but felt, before she saw, that avenue of escape evaporate in the dust of crashing boot steps. So she veered quickly, running at full speed. While her close vision was excellent, her distance vision was not as acute. Sensing by the feel of increasing vibration as much as sight, she knew her situation had become almost instantly desperate. And her confusion cost her critical seconds. . .

"Oh God! Get it! Kill it!" the shrieking voice demanded.

Reptilian instincts required her to use precious energy to veer once again as boots closed the distance. . .

"Yes Your Highness! I see it Your Highness! Guards! Toward the west wall!"

The vibrations told her before her small eyes confirmed it; her usual avenue of escape was cut off. That she was trapped did not consciously register to the lizard. That would require a conclusion, implying a mind that worked on a different level. Hers still labored to try and discriminate between the different sets of foot falls. Perhaps she could find a way between them. . .

Suddenly a battle axe cut the ground beside her. An ancient instinct, an evolutionary miracle of deception, automatically engaged. Somewhere a signal was sent, and a cell next to a neighboring cell released itself. Then another, and another, joined in a futile bid for life; and in less than one of her quick heartbeats, thousands more followed a primal reaction for survival by disengaging from their neighbors. And she left her tail behind her as she moved quickly off. In their last moments of something between life and death, the cells caused the tail to move as if alive. But the humans would not be fooled. And the lizard had no delusions about that. . .

She had no delusions, and as her fate was being resolved she even knew something of the fate that had somehow twisted in upon her ancestors like the very helix of DNA that had once taken a departing turn and allowed soft flesh to replace the infinitely more practical armor of scales. Her eyes winked closed, then open with fatigue. But for a quirk of genetics it was they who had digits that allowed them to grasp more than just rocks. . .

Now the heavy footfalls came from in front of her again. But much closer. Much. She could not keep this up for long. She was quicker, but the humans had more stamina. . .

"Here! Over here!" The deep voice resonated with the monstrous pounding of feet. Many feet. With so many vibrations around her she was starting to become confused. She knew she was in mortal danger. Suddenly a boot nearly crushed her. And she veered again. Her lungs burned in their bid for oxygen as she raced off. The blinding dust was adding to her confusion.

"I see it!" She had nowhere to go. But her primal instincts precluded any thought of surrender. She didn't even know the option existed. So she ran. She just ran. Choking on dust, slow with fatigue, she ran in futile circles. She ran until. . .

Suddenly she could not move. Her feet were instantly paralyzed. And she stopped.

Her nervous system was not highly developed enough to feel true pain. Had it been, she would have been in agony. Instead she only knew a strange immobility. . .

"I got it, sir!"

"Quick, help me with the Queen. Damn thing came so close to her she fainted. Guards!"

The footfalls congregated in a single direction. And the lizard, very weak now, did not move. Could not move. The spear that pinned her to the dry earth, nearly cutting her in two, seemed to put a metallic taste in her mouth. She found that taste disagreeable. So foreign. And for a moment she contemplated that instead of contemplating her fate.

"Is it dead?"

"Yes, Your Highness."

"Thank God. Help me in now. But be sure there is no sign of the ugly creature by the time I take my morning constitution. I thought you told me. . . "

As the high voice faded out of the lizard's hearing she knew this one was different. The red trailing from the high hat indicated that; but there was something more. This one seemed to embrace a fear of her species beyond the others who came to the garden. And the lizard found that puzzling. Yet she knew she had little time left to puzzle. . .

As she lay there dying, the stench of burning flesh wafted in through the rock wall and filled her nostrils. And while she could not comprehend the historical significance of these times, she did know that it was a very dark era for the humans. After all, she could smell fear and chaos as well as she could smell food or a mate. And she could not help but smell the death that prevailed in every direction beyond the garden. Yet she knew they would continue to survive and dominate. . . for now.

She knew the destiny of her species as well as her own destiny. That her kind would continue to decline, becoming smaller, and fewer, in a world burgeoning with the technology of mills that were driven by water, saddles with stirrups, armor that was made of metal. So lizards had even less prominence in a future that had been determined very long ago. With a brain so simple and primeval as hers, she could not help but know something of her species' destiny. It was as obvious to her as her history.

As the light dimmed the temperature dropped and she experienced a sensation she rarely felt. Cold. But immobile as she was, she could do nothing about it. Beneath her, red blood siphoned away. Gray eggs spilled out of her body. And she was very tired. As she lay there in the fading light her thoughts flew to a new place, inspired by a new image. Her eyes blinked closed, then open again for the last time.

In the twilight she saw her first star. And then she noticed another. With difficulty she turned her head a few degrees. They were captivating. After all, she was normally long since within the protection of her underground refuge by now. Yet her primal brain knew something about stars in a mysterious, predictive way. She even knew that the first visitor from one of those distant specks would be more like her than the soft fleshy being that had murdered her. And they would be able to grasp more than mere rocks.

Primordial visions of ancestry and destiny filled her last thoughts. And she found them strangely satisfying and sublime. As she died, she wondered if she were the first reptile to smile. . .

Bluebells
Teresa Brandt

When my mother is rested and happy, her eyes are the color of bluebells. During late March in England, bluebell flowers carpet the forest and unfarmed hillsides. Each blossom is a bell, a delicate inverted cup the color of a late summer sky rolling over acres of mature cornfields. Or a sky on a day after the rains have stopped and the clouds have dissipated leaving only the pure open blue, unadorned and simple in its beauty. The petals are the color of periwinkle, reminding me of cold water lapping over a pool of shallow rocks beside a shore of snow. It is the blue of smooth, silk dresses and spring tablecloths. In full bloom, these blue cups tilt toward the sky, and the earth of the meadow is hidden beneath them.

As an eleven-year-old, I stood at the edge of the forest meadows feasting on their color. I took the bucket used for scrubbing to gather them for the house. My mother's home was lacking in softness. Beauty took a back seat to the basic necessity of caring for her ten children.

Then in mother's life, there was never a day with time included for picking and arranging flowers. Children had to be awakened, breakfasts made and supervised. Mornings were filled with piles of laundry to be washed and ironed, floors to be swept and beds to be made. Dinner was such a tremendous feat to accomplish, its beginnings were initiated right after breakfast. My mother's crowning achievement was clean, fed and clothed children sent off to school.

The bluebells started at the edge of the trees. As I entered the woods, my legs became tangled in the clusters of their stalks. Crouching into a sea of blue, I found the base of each flower, gently bent its stalk, and twisted it loose. Milky nectar oozed over my fingers and down my forearm like pancake syrup from a toddler's hand. I held the flowers close to my eyes to inspect the little bells as they shook in the breeze. They shook like the bells around the necks of cows walking through a pasture. Then carefully, to prevent crushing them, I placed each long stem into the bucket so the blossoms poked out of the top.

On the way to a full bucket, I examined the hairy moss on the barks of trees and the other gifts the woods offered. In between picking bluebells, my sticky hands cradled fallen chestnuts from the autumn before, cracking their hulls and rubbing the shiny boot-brown nut underneath. My flower gathering led me to the hollows between the hills where I found walls built with the dead branches of trees, scattered rocks and debris of the forest floor.

Eventually, the bucket was full, and I skipped home with it swinging from my arm as if I were a milk maid in a fairy tale. I took out my mother's two empty flower vases and filled them for the dining room table and the bookcase in the living room. After these were arranged, I stooped down to the cupboard where my mother kept empty jars; jars used for everything from leftover dinner vegetables to serving as fish bowls for the brown fish we caught in the pond on the other side of the woods. I picked fat jars with large openings. When I tucked the bluebells inside them, they were transformed into wide-mouthed jars of crystal. The stalks showed straight and strong through their sides, and the bursts of blossoms sprayed an overgrown bouquet over their ridges.

Once the bucket was emptied, every room in the house was accented by a bouquet of bluebell . . . on a dresser, table or windowsill. My mother passed me as I stood back to admire them. Her eyes creased in appreciation. I remember, at that moment, her irises were the same hue as the petals of the bluebells, even though she wasn't rested and had a whole list of things to do that day.

etiquette
Alison Anastasio

asks the wolf,
"what brings you here?"
answers the rabbit,
"why, i came for a visit.
may i have a seat?"
replies the wolf,
"of course! what kind of
host
do you take me for?"
says the rabbit,
"thank you so.
shall i stay for tea?"
returns the wolf,
"certainly!
what kind of
host
do you take me for?
do stay for supper as well."
comments the rabbit,
"quite a generous
host
i would say.
i would be honored.
what will you be serving?"
answers the smirking wolf,
"why rabbit of course!
what kind of
host
do you take me for?"

What Did You Say?

Cynthia Berkenmeier

"Hi, I'm calling about the appointment card we just received in the mail." "Yes," the pleasant voice responds. "The appointment is for my husband with the neurology department." Silence. "Can you tell me who requested this appointment to be made for my husband?" "Let me pull the file; hold for one moment and I will research this matter for you." "Thank you," I muttered as music starts to play in the background. I am not paying attention. My mind is swirling with a long parade of doctors, psychiatrists, emergency rooms, aging parents, and people I love breaking down in the prime of life. Fear, concern and confusion grow like wildfire inside by head. I want to cry. The woman comes back on the line. "This appointment was scheduled by Dr. Taures, a physician in the emergency room of the Walnut Creek facility. He ordered this appointment as a result of your husband's last visit." "Thank you for the information." I hang up the telephone, scared.

I sit down at the kitchen table. John's words of the recent visit with his parents rush into my mind. "Mom is doing much better. Apparently, there is something wrong with her thyroid gland, and they have stared her on some medication. Dad looks terrible, very pale, and he told me he lost twenty-five pounds in the last two months." "What did you say?" "That's right, now dad is sick. He secretly told me he has been having dizzy spells." We looked into each other's eyes and saw fear and disbelief. "I gave my dad a hug. He actually hugged me back. Then I went into the garage to use his table saw. Dad followed me. Remember how the garage used to be filled with electronic repair equipment and power tools for working with wood?" I nod sadly to myself as this conversation of the night before won't stop playing in my head. "Now the garage is almost empty. The bench is totally cleared off. The only power tool left is the table saw. I fired up the old table saw and dad asks me in a shout, 'Can I help?' I told him to just keep me company. Then Dad says the weirdest thing, 'If I fall down just pick me back up.'"

The look on John's face is vivid in my memory. The tears welled up in the corners of his eyes as he continued to recount Sunday's visit with his parents. "So I fired up the saw and started to work. I looked at Dad every few minutes just to make sure he hadn't started to get dizzy or fallen down. The strangest thing was that every time I looked at Dad he was looking at his watch. He looked at his watch at least six times in thirty minutes. He had this sort of scared look on his face. Finally I asked him why he kept looking at his watch. He told me, 'Karen is supposed to be here at 3 p.m. She's late.'"

My brow furrowed just like it had the night before. John and I had come to the conclusion that his parents could no longer drive by themselves. Now they were relying heavily on Karen, John's older sister who kept a room at the parent's home. John and I both knew that his father was far too proud to call 911 in case of an emergency. The look on John's face was starting to scare me. I wondered if he was going to have another attack, a panic attack as labeled by Dr. Taures in the emergency room of the Walnut Creek facility.

"Are you OK, Honey?" "No, not really." "It's OK to cry if you want to." His bottom lip trembles and I hug him tightly. "I bet you're sad. I remember when my mom told me of her diagnosis of emphysema, I was very sad." I watched for signs of another panic attack in John. I remember telling him that no matter what happens, I'll always be there for him.

Now, in retrospect, I'm unsure of how accurate my promise was. To this day the shrill of oncoming sirens still constantly sounds in my memory. Just two months ago, I walked in my home one Friday evening, opened the door, and told John, "I think I'm having a heart attack. Please watch the boys while I call 911." "What did you say?" I never did answer him. The paramedics were at our home in less than three minutes.

As I sit here in my kitchen on this sunny morning, I feel so overwhelmed. The stories keep playing over and over in my head. My best friend, husband, myself, brothers and sister-in-law, neighbors too, all breaking down in the prime of life. My mom and dad both in poor health but still full of unstoppable spirit. Now John's parents getting sick too. I sip my cup of tea and search my tranquilized mind for answers why everyone around me is breaking down. I rationalize that our parents are aging and it is natural for them to get old and weak as time takes its toll. The thing that was so troubling was that seemingly healthy thirty- and forty-year-old people were having this problem labeled "panic attacks." I theorize that since the invention of the computer, everything has shifted into high gear. I now schedule my appointment and activities in blocks of minutes, instead of hours like in days gone by. Alcohol, Valium, and physical violence. Now I think I understand. I think I'm so smart, a rapid increase in responsibilities, choices and decisions to be made in split seconds. All this weight on the same shoulders of human beings who evolved from apes millions of years ago. Now with a minimum of hair and walking on two feet. No, no, no. This is getting me nowhere. My hands start to shake. Tears begin to roll down my cheeks. Should I call the psychiatrist I'm working with? My head is spinning. Did I take my medication this morning? Do I need more medication? Who can I call to come help me? "I found it, Mommy," a little voice from the living room jolts me back to reality. Thoughts of sadness and confusion still dancing in my head. "Did you see that, Mommy?" "Sorry, Honey, I was just thinking. What did you say?"

The Mixing Bowl
Blanche Abrams

Grandma lived in an era when women had ten children and remained at home to raise them. She experienced nothing of life — save the constant creating and maintaining of it.

At precisely 3:15 each day, I would stop at Grandma's house on my way home from school. Opening the back door, I walked up the stairs into the enclosed porch, removed my shoes, set down my book bag and opened the inside door. Here's Grandma, her back facing me, her arm making circular motions. I know she's fixing something in her large, blue and white speckled mixing bowl like she does every day.

Her hair is short, ending just above her collar. It's shiny silver and looks like it could glow in the dark. Her back still towards me, she says, "Did you learn anything from your teacher today?" I always reply, "Yes, ma'am." I notice her long-sleeved, oatmeal-colored undershirt beneath her blue and purple flowered cotton dress. Her coffee-colored, rolled-up stockings show beneath the hemline. They seem to fall down farther, the later the day becomes. You can practically tell time by them. Heavy, black, thick-soled shoes support her varicose legs.

"Help yourself to a lemon drop from the pantry," she says.

"Thank you, Grandma. Grandma?"

"Yes?"

"Whatcha fixin' in ya kitchen?"

"Dough for apple slices."

"Mmmm, my favorite."

I smelled bread baking in the oven, chicken soup simmering on the stove, and the raisin-rice pudding cooling on the side board. The kitchen was very plain and small. A porcelain sink with a side rack for draining and drying dishes, and a white stove and refrigerator. There were very few cupboards and no counter space. The sparse room contained a small rectangular table pushed against the wall to conserve space, and it was here that she spent her days.

I sat watching her repetitive movements as she sifted flour and kneaded the dough. She was a large-boned Ukrainian woman. It was difficult to say if she still had her figure due to the layers of concealing clothing. The fact that her right breast had been removed years earlier went undetected. When she put her arms around you — you were lost in the complete softness and warmth of her.

Her face belied her years. Gardenia-white skin held taut by high cheekbones. The only creases in her face were at the corners of her twinkling eyes. There was a string around her neck. With a slight tug, a change purse appeared from within the recesses of her chest. It was necessary for her to hide money from Grandpa. If he found it, he would head for the newsstand at 65th and Central and bet on his favorite horse.

The scent of Grandma was somewhere between Vicks and BenGay. She used either one or the other depending on her ailment. I found her a few times rubbing BenGay on her knees as she cried. It was becoming more difficult for her body to support her long days.

Her children came and went between jobs, college, friends, and parties. They were immersed in the time where parents fade into the background and friends reign supreme. Raised during the Depression, they were after more than their parents could give them, and they wanted it today. Her married children owned more than she did but didn't pitch in to buy her a modern washing machine and dryer. They never took her on a vacation or out for a fancy dinner. They were too busy to notice she was getting old.

It bothers me that Grandma never felt pearls against her skin, never knew the softness of Hawaiian sand beneath her feet or savored the texture of buttered lobster.

She was alone when her heart stopped. Aunt Jean found her laying on the kitchen floor, her wooden spoon still in her hand. The speckled blue mixing bowl lay broken beside her. They had both served a lifetime of wear.

I'll never forget when it happened. A Saturday. No school. One of the days I hadn't stopped by to say, "Hey Grandma, whatcha fixin' in ya kitchen?"

The Gift
Kathryn Lechner

The silver bell above the door jingled, disrupting the quiet of the afternoon. A customer. Hiram Green lowered the Sunday section of the Times and peered over the top of the paper. The door inched forward. Dropping his feet from the counter, he snapped the newspaper shut and dropped it on the floor beside him. Standing up, he tucked in his shirt, straightened his tie, and put on a smile. The bell rang again. He moved from behind the counter so he could get a clear view of the door. His smile faded. A young, black girl stood on the threshold, pushing the door back and forth, ringing the bell, her small brown face tipped up, smiling, watching it.

"Quit dinging that thing. Jesus, ain't you never seen a bell before?"

She jumped at the sound of his voice. "Hey, Mr. Green."

Hiram sighed and crossed the room. Grabbing hold of the door, he pushed it wide open. The bell dinged one more time. They both looked up at it.

"Marygrace — I told you a hundred times — I don't want you in my shop. Now get the hell outta here 'for I call Sheriff Pepper."

"I jus' come for the vase, suh."

"You ain't got no two dollars. Now go on, git."

"But I do. I been savin' and now I got it."

"Savin'? Savin' how?"

She held up two fingers pinched closely together. "Every week I been puttin' jus' a little bit away."

He narrowed his eyes at her suspiciously. "You expect me to believe you done saved up a whole two dollars?"

"Yes, suh. I done got it right here." She patted the pocket of her faded, navy dress. The faint jingle of coin confirmed her statement.

"Well, shit." Two dollars was two dollars.

Sticking his head out the door, he quickly checked the neighborhood. Ollie Enneking's hound bounded down the street in hot pursuit of an orange and black barn cat. He could see Milo Edison, sound asleep across the road, his feet propped up on a pickle barrel, chair tipped back and his mouth wide open in a snore.

Sunday afternoons always were deader than all get out. Clearing his throat loudly, Hiram pushed the door shut.

"Now this has got to be the last time you come in here Marygrace, you understand that?"

"Oh yes, suh."

"If anybody saw you come in here, I'd be in a helluvalotta trouble."

"I understand. Nobody saw me. I slipped in quiet as a mouse."

"There is a sign right out front."

"Yes, suh, I know that. But I cain't read."

"Don't be pullin' none of that bullshit with me, young lady, you know what it says."

"Yes, suh, I do. It says 'No niggers allowed.'"

"That's right."

"But you let me come in here before, an' I knowed you have Mam's birthday present. You been savin' it for me all this time."

"Marygrace — ,"

"An' since I cain't read, I jus' figured it would be okay this one last time."

He cleared his throat again. Hell. He wished she'd quit staring at him with those goddamn brown eyes. What was it about this little girl? Why did she always seem to be getting the better of him? Well, he was going to fix her this time, fix her good.

"I don't mean to be no trouble, Mr. Green." She took two steps towards him. She was quite a sight with her nappy black hair tied into two little braids that stuck out at the sides of her head. Her little blue dress had been patched so many times there must have been eight different fabrics covering it. Her feet were bare, filthy with dirt. His polished wood floor was covered with her dusty little footprints.

"It's jus' so beautiful in here — all glittery and sparkly." She lowered her head and crooked her finger at him. He bent forward to hear. "It's like buried treasure," she whispered, her eyes wide and luminous. She lifted her head, gazing about the room, letting her eyes drink in every bauble and trinket.

He watched the expression on her face, intrigued with the play of emotions that swept across it. Following her glance about the room, he could suddenly see it through her eyes. The sun, shining in through the plate glass window, bounced off the vases and crystal bowls creating a sparkling illusion of riches. The afternoon light, through the quivering lamp shade prisms, cast sun-dipped rainbows that danced across the walls. The mirrors caught and reflected the scene, until the whole room did seem to sparkle and shine, like diamonds in a mine, like buried treasure.

He shook his head, snapping the spell.

"Shit. I ain't got time to be listenin' to none of your crap."

"I ain't funnin' with you, Mr. Green. It's the God's honest truth."

"That's what you said last time."

"But I got the money now."

"Well —,"

"Oh please, Mr. Green, it's for Mam's birthday."

"All right, all right. Jus' don't touch nuthin', ya hear?"

"Yes, suh, Mr. Green."

He gave her what he hoped was a good hard look, then turned on his heel and made his way to the back room.

Them niggers was always coming in and bothering him. Mildred said it was because he was too soft. She said he should keep a shotgun behind the counter and point it at 'em whenever they ventured in. That would keep 'em away. On the other hand, he would argue with himself, their money spent just as good as any white man's. With this depression going on, they needed every dollar they could muster.

Kicking the boxes out of his way, he moved through the storeroom to the back window. Reaching up, he plucked the small vase from the window sill. It was still warm from the noonday sun. He ran his finger along the crack. The glue had turned a dingy yellow. Yes sir, he'd fixed her good. That stupid little nigger had picked out the white porcelain bud vase that had been broken then glued last winter. He'd put it on clearance this spring. With his thumbnail, he scraped the twenty cent price tag off the bottom. Smiling to himself he walked back out into the showroom. The little nigger was walking about the room, eyes big as moons, her hands clasped under her chin.

He cleared his throat.

"I got it here."

She turned about. Smiling, she crossed the room to him.

"Oh thank you, Mr. Green. I be much obliged."

"Yeah, yeah. Let's just hurry this on up."

"Can I see it?"

"I s'pose." He handed it to her.

He was ready with an argument if she said anything about the vase's appearance. He knew it had faded considerably in the hot summer sun. And the glue had yellowed. But she had made him hold it for her, with no money down. Served her right.

"Oh, it's jus' as beautiful as I remembered it."

"Hrmmph."

"Mam is going to be so excited."

"That's jus' wonderful. I'm so happy for you. Now give me my money and git on out of here."

"But I already done give it to you." She pointed towards the cash register. "It's there, on the counter."

He turned to look. A small mountain of pennies sat piled on the counter.

"Two hundred pennies." She beamed broadly. "I counted every one."

He stood speechless, staring at the pennies, then turned back around. "Oh, now — you jus' wait one minute."

He had hesitated too long. She was gone, the silver bell dinging against the door.

She stopped and turned at the window, smiling, her white teeth sparkling in her brown face. Bringing her arm up she waved. He automatically raised his hand to wave back, before he realized what he was doing. Scowling, he dismissed her with a slap in the air. Damn niggers. Turning on his heel he crossed to the counter and began picking the pennies up, one by one.

Surrealistic Feelings
Valerie Nebo

Surrealistic feelings
Upon the vague soul
Mutated in impressionists colors
Spiraling downward
Into the sabled chasm
Emotions stripped and whipped
And bared
Upon the cross
Of a crew-cut Christ
Suspended by square pegs
Adorned with icons
Of modern times
Altered memories
Melting
In the hands
Of the Dozen Marked Faces
Sagging in despair
Crying
The shades of blue
Given their own identity
Only to form
More altered shapes
More faces
Not faces
Not anything
Yet everything
Everything confuses
We cower from confusion
Yet will pay
Any price

Suspicious Paths
Aletha Dier

On the other side of Pleasanton Ridge, off a trail I've rarely seen another soul on, is a tiny abandoned house with boarded up doors and broken windows. It looks like it may have been built for a ranch-hand in the '50's, and has holes in the roof and rats on the floor. It has a certain musty smell and is surrounded by waist-high thistles.

Since my hiking partner and I discovered it three years ago, jokingly referring to it as "our summer home," we've never seen another human there. Occasionally there are cattle milling about the area. We discovered the cattle trail led over a knoll to a muddy pond, where once we frightened away some surprised ducks as we suddenly came over the knoll. I never saw the ducks again, and speculate they were migrating.

My hiking partner and I hiked here at the Ridge an average of three times a week for two years. About eighty percent of the time we'd end up at this old house to stand on the dilapidated front porch and gaze at the phenomenal view. The old structure itself was unimpressive, but a wealthy man would pay top dollar to come home to this view every night.

The pristine, softly sloping hillside and plateaus below the porch were full of trees and birds and cattle. An eroded rain wash gave way to a creek that ran fairly full in the winter. Palomares Canyon Road lay at the bottom of the hill, though you couldn't actually see it from here. Up the other side were perfectly planted old groves of olive, walnut, and fruit trees. Far off to the left, one could see Highway 680 where the expansive nurseries and Sunol Golf Course stretched for brightly colorful miles.

But there was no sound from the highway this far above it. Semi-trucks were small dots. Birds dominated the audible world here. This evening I stood alone on this isolated spot, taking in the view as sunset approached rapidly. There was always something unusual about the thick bushy area below and the olive grove and chaparral above the trail leading here. For several acres, there were vague paths weaving in and out of the bushes — too thick for cattle to pass through.

No, the only creature I figured low enough to the ground to make these well-worn paths were ground squirrels. And yes, there were holes and occasional ground squirrels running about, but I'd never seen ground squirrels carve such distinct paths. Some of those holes were just too large for squirrels anyway.

Often my hiking partner and I would hear a rustling in this dense overgrowth. We'd peer into the bush where the noise came from, but the most we ever saw were lizards and birds.

My well-weathered hiker's sense told me there was something vaguely suspect about this particular area. Tonight I was about to find out why.

Having just left the abandoned house, my peripheral vision caught a dark, low movement in the chaparral in the olive grove above me. I felt for my mace in my pocket. I looked up to see a brown fox with nervous eyes shifting from me to his comrades. His comrades! Three or four other adult foxes were slinking out of sight into the chaparral. A pack of them! The obvious one hesitated a while, long enough for me to get a good long look at his beautiful fur, sleek body structure, brown and reddish face, and that famous tail. I drank the sight in and crystallized it in my mind — he was only 20, 25 feet away — before he disappeared into the chaparral.

GOD'S NATURE REVEALED TO ME! I silently climbed up off the trail into the old olive grove which was planted so long ago that, according to a naturalist I spoke to, no one knows who planted it. I searched the chaparral to see where the pack disappeared, but saw nothing. I knelt down on the exact spot where the magnificent creature had stood less than a minute before, looking for droppings or tracks. Perhaps they were eating a ground squirrel or lizard up here, but no bones, fur, nothing. Suddenly a rustling and a sharp warning bark! I looked up to see a large fox with a gray face bounding toward me where I knelt!

This was NOT the shy, elusive brown fox, warily slinking into the bushes that one imagines if one were ever fortunate enough to encounter these rare, secretive creatures.

I got up and ran down the trail. Was it protecting young? Was it rabid? Although I was outnumbered, I couldn't imagine the pack attacking anything as large as a human! It ran down after me onto the trail, but then it ran about 10 feet in front of me. Actually, it did not appear too concerned about me, as it instead seemed to be looking for its comrades. Again it paused long enough for me to get an incredibly close look before it slipped into the underbrush below the trail.

There was a tremendous amount of rustling around in those bushes as I passed near them. But peer as I might, I saw nothing more.

I KNEW it was more than ground squirrels! But why hadn't I figured foxes? I had heard them a year and a half ago. It was winter, dusk at a lower plateau on the east side of the Ridge. My partner and I had a favorite sycamore tree where we would sit in the low branches and enjoy the view from there.

Silently we approached the tree. There on the other side of it was a deer — a BUCK no less — who sighted us at the exact moment we did him. The three of us stood frozen in time as the last of the sun's rays fell upon his young antlers — just 15 feet from where we stood!

He then snorted so fiercely we thought he would charge us. Instead he cautiously, gracefully slipped away into the tall grass and trees.

About ten minutes later as we sat in the branches, silently reliving that mystical moment in our minds, the silence was broken by a sharp bark. Then more barks. Then in unison — an eerie howl. We peered into the grove of trees roughly 40 yards up the hill where the wild sound came from, but we never saw anything.

Three years of hiking here during every season. Not once had I seen the elusive fox, until this magic evening. Never again will I casually pass rustling bushes, assuming birds or lizards. Don't be surprised if you see me on the trail intently peering into bushes and olive groves and chaparral — searching for these magnificent creatures — the foxes of Pleasanton Ridge!

Guernica
Fred Norman

The painting *Guernica* hangs in a special annex of the Prado in Madrid. A little girl and her grandmother entered the museum one day and stood before it. They stood in silence for several minutes as if transfixed by the scene in front of them. It confused the little girl, and eventually she looked up at her grandmother and asked, "What is this called, Abuelita?"

"It is called *Guernica*," her grandmother replied.

This further confused the little girl. "It doesn't look like Guernica," she said. "We live in Guernica, and it doesn't look like this."

"It is a Guernica that used to be," said the woman in a voice much older than a grandmother could ever be.

"Is it a painting, Abuelita?" asked the little girl.

"It is," replied the older voice, "but it is more than that." And after several silent moments, "It is art," she said, now smiling sadly at the little girl.

"I do not understand," complained the little girl. "Is every painting art?"

"Oh, no," said Abuelita. "Paintings are mere copies of a shape, the outside that our eyes can see. Art has depth. It forces us to look inside our souls. It is seen by minds and felt by hearts. It is..."

"It is ugly," said the little girl in frustrated interruption.

"Yes, this is ugly art," her grandmother agreed. "But not all art is ugly. Inside our souls are many things, both deep and shallow, strong and weak. Inside are feelings of happiness and sadness, emotions of love and hate, prayers of life and fears of death. A painting that stimulates a memory of happiness is pretty. A painting that caresses dreams of love is beautiful. A painting that depicts a loving granddaughter smiling in the future is wondrous indeed. Nor must it be a painting. Words and melodies can get inside the soul. Anything created by the hand and mind of Man is art if it touches that which makes a being human. If it touches love and life, it is the art of happiness; if it touches hate and death, as this art does, it is the art of ugliness."

"Oh, I would like the happy art," said the little girl excitedly. "Why must we look at this?"

"Because I am in the painting," the old, old voice replied, "and I must see if you are, too."

The little girl stared tensely at the painting. She walked back and forth its width as if inspecting every drop of paint. At least five minutes passed before she whispered to her grandmother, "No, Abuelita, you are wrong. I do not see you there, and I do not see me, either."

"What do you see?" her grandmother asked gently.

"I see a bull with misplaced eyes."

"Yes, that is Spain."

"A crazy, screaming horse."

"The conquerors."

"Gray smoke."

"The air we breathed."

"Brown walls."

"The color of our world back then."

"People, many people, white like death, crying, hurt, in agony."

"You see my friends."

"I see a baby. Dead. Oh, God! A poor dead baby hanging from its mother's arms."

"You see your mother's brother," a rasping echo sounded from the depths of ancient memories, "and you see me."

Tears burst from deep inside the little girl, cascaded down her cheeks, and stained her blouse. She screamed, "I hate this painting!" and turned her back to it. "I will not look at it again," she said with a stubbornness almost adult in tone, certain in its finality, mistaken in its certainty.

"But you must look at it," her grandmother implored. "For it is art. It connects you to the past and it will shape your future. It teaches you the truth and prepares you for the lies ahead. It is knowledge overcoming ignorance. It is the guarantor of love and life and happiness. It is the link between your grandmother and you."

The little girl turned back to face the painting. Still crying, she inspected it as before, walking back and forth in front of it, exploring every stroke of meaning, absorbing every color of emotion, tracing every form, erasing every preconception, living in the past, traveling to the future, where, and whence, she spoke. "I see you, Abuelita," said a youthful voice that was not the voice of a little girl, "but I do not see me."

They left the Prado annex holding hands, and together stepped from shadows into brilliant sunshine. Shading her eyes, Abuelita looked up at the sky and saw no planes of war. The little girl looked at the sky and saw a flock of brightly colored birds. Both smiled. Their faces glowed.

A Day in Hiroshima
Lauren Hirshberg

On August 6th 1945, a distant land embraced our dangers,
Life would tragically change for this group of foreign strangers.
It began in Hiroshima, as the peaceful noon drew near,
Sun shone upon thousands of people soon to disappear.
A village could be seen with market products stacked in piles,
Walking amid these lively streets were families, colored with bright smiles.

Suddenly, a sound was heard; so loud it deafened the ears,
and a blinding light showered the sky, clouding over a thousand tears.
Instantly, 70 thousand perished from the burn of this atomic blast,
Lives that had merely begun few years before now remained in the past.

Those who survived the initial explosion faced a horrifying fate,
as they observed their bodies (melting from flames) begin to mutate.
The remainder of the survivors suffered disease by radiation,
and became victims to the consequences of mistakes made by their nation.

How ironic that these victims had not even voted in the polls,
and chosen these empowered leaders; yet they paid the death tolls.
Did these leaders understand this massive force that they had taken for granted
As it determined the thousands of graves the blast had naturally planted.

The power to destroy a nation had been demonstrated by the United States,
and so began the starting gunshot in the World Nuclear race.
Who would be the first to construct the most efficient killing machine?
To further intimidate others, and forbid all to intervene.
It would prove to be too late before the world powers would realize,
that we cannot control this power to play god, through unselfish eyes.

Walk With A Feather
Kirk Ridgeway

I found the feather of a hawk
And walked with it.

I felt its edge cut into wind
Lifting and falling
with each twist I gave.
I felt its weight become weightless
When the pitch was just right
And the air flowed smoothly.

For an hour I played
and became the bird,
Sensing each change of now
Responding to each new movement
Feeling the pleasure of feathers.

Now I watch the hawks
Circling, swooping, gliding.
I watch them adjust their wings
Flap to change their course
Float on wind.

Because I walked with a feather
I know the feeling of flight
The hawk
The wind.
Because I sit on this log
Silently watching
And alone
I know these things.

When Pigs Flew
Janella Sanchez-Salazar

I remember the day Farmer Jones found his sow in the chicken coop. Apparently, the sow had been sneaking out to the hen house every night to meet with the rooster. Well, when Spring came along, Betsy, the sow, gave birth to a beautiful pink piglet with feathery white wings. People from miles away flocked to Farmer Jones' place to catch a glimpse of this fascinating creature. That's what started the fetish for flying pigs.

Farmers everywhere bred their roosters with their pigs. Everyone was entranced by this new species of animal. Scientists pondered the dilemma of whether a pig with wings was a fowl or a mammal. The next surprise came when Betsy's daughter, Polly, was chasing a mouse and all of a sudden, took flight! Thereafter, Polly was known as "Polly the Flying Pig." All the farmers who had pigs with wings couldn't wait until they, too, had pigs that flew!

Soon enough, the world was covered with flying pigs. The farmers didn't have the means to keep the flying pigs confined to the farm, so they were free and wild everywhere. Flying pigs mated with other flying pigs and the population exploded. Since flying pigs were so difficult to capture, pork, ham, bologna, and bacon prices soared (no pun intended). People on the street had to carry umbrellas or wear very wide brimmed hats to protect themselves from the frequent pig residuals.

Restaurants no longer served eggs and bacon; all they could afford was eggs and beef patties. Former duck hunters hid in "pig blinds" to shoot at the flying pigs. Unfortunately, their golden retrievers were soon tired of retrieving huge, heavy pigs from rivers and lakes, so the dogs went on strike. After all, chasing and retrieving pigs had never been in their contracts.

The stress on air traffic controllers increased immeasurably. It was difficult to monitor the erratic aerial movements of the pigs, so the controllers sometimes sent planes right up into a herd of flying pigs with disastrous results. In fact, huge swarms of pigs frequently swept over the skies, practically eclipsing the sun. They were like monstrous black clouds blowing over whole cities at a time.

There was a positive side to this new era of flying porkies. Instead of having highways patrolled by aircraft, some civic-minded pigs became trained in the profession of pigcraft. This saved the government many millions of dollars, and the redirected tax monies went toward housing the homeless. Homeless people were given jobs, food, clothing, and a new chance to live away from the threat of overhead pig bombardment which they had suffered in their former uncovered street habitats.

Another benefit of the existence of flying pigs was the decrease in landfills and garbage piles. The pigs that were caught, but not killed, were (after clipping their wings, of course) shipped out to the landfills. You can't imagine all the things that flying pigs will actually eat! They ate rotten food, newspaper, boxes and even plastic. When word got out to all the other free range flying pigs that there were places where they wouldn't ever have to stop eating, pigs, even pot bellied pigs from China, flocked to the U.S.A. There was a huge feeding frenzy. Eventually, all the landfills were gone except for one. Trash from everywhere was placed in this one huge landfill. There was garbage from Mexico, Europe, even Australia. The pigs were all quite content with this situation, so all was well.

After eating all that trash, the amount of pig deposits was enormous. There were literally mountains of it. This is where the farmers were rewarded for creating these amazing creatures. The droppings made perfect fertilizer. Fruits and vegetables grew to be gigantic, and the quantity of it all was so great that there was no more world hunger. The food grown with this fertilizer was so plentiful, delicious, and pleasing, the U.S. couldn't help but share with all the other countries. In a blink, world hunger was demolished by those wonderful, lovable flying pigs.

Given what we knew about the superior intelligence of pigs over that of other animals, we should have guessed what was going to happen next. The ability to fly over state capitols and Washington, D.C., caused the flying pigs to interact on the political scene. Everything changed; pigs were the White House pet now. There were no more "First Family" cats or dogs! Poor "Socks" was kicked out of the presidential kennel and was forced to live in the outside world. All the presidents looked to their pigs, not their beloved wives, for advice. Flying pigs became members of royal and high power families everywhere. There was even one in the

Mafia. Many people began to believe that this had been Betsy's idea from the time she started seeing that gall darn rooster. Even more people worried that Betsy's children and grandchildren would soon take over the earth.

All good things must come to an end, including the flying pigs. Overexcited hunters from the National Rifle Association shot down flying pigs for sport wherever they saw them. The population of flying pigs decreased slowly but surely. Flying pigs had brought an end to our human problem of the land filling with garbage and refuse. We brought it back when we wiped them out of existence. Flying pigs had brought an end to homelessness, but, with the death of the species, the human race brought that back, too. Flying pigs had ended world hunger; without them, the world found itself starving, again, for what it could not have. People just couldn't live with the specter of pigs becoming equals, so they destroyed their race. Humans ended the best thing that ever happened to them. The flying pigs are gone; all attempts to bring them back have been unsuccessful, and now the world is worse off than it was before.

The Old Man In The Park
Jerry Gervase

Listen.
Listen!
Hear him coming,
muffled shuffling
scruffy shoes.
Metal cane tip —
tip, tip, tapping,
dot dot dashing
to scampering squirrels,
in the gravelly scree.
Vigilant leaves eaves —
drop, to hear his
murmured greetings.
And as he passes,
gossiping grasses
bow,
bend low,
and pigeons stretch
their nodding necks
to see if it is him.
It is!

It is!
Then when
the noble bench
presents her
slatted lap
to receive her
Royal Guest,
his subjects
gather at
his feet
to
pick
the
pods
of
peanuts
from
his
palm.

Tea Tree

Carolyn Cogan

I once loved a ficus tree
that made her singular forest
in our living room

She died slowly
of a persistent, parasitic
stickiness

I get attached to the beings
I love
I'm a one-plant, one-cat,
one-person
woman
loyal in life
and long after death

For months the corner
where the ficus had stood
remained
empty

Then one day my partner brought home
a tea tree
distant cousin of the banana
or bamboo —

strong and exotic —

with a slender tropical trunk
and long lop-eared leaves
like a jade jackrabbit

I barely noticed this strange
interloper
until today when
dipping her green leather paddles
in the breeze
she whispered to me
"I love it here"

Taunting Mr. Kingsley
Teresa Brandt

Saturday was the day Claire's mother took her to Cornhill Market. They waited at the wooden bus stop for the red double-decker bus which arrived tardily after eight a.m. Side by side they sat for the forty minute ride to town propping empty market baskets on their laps.

Claire noticed a hat that looked familiar, four rows ahead in the opposite aisle. It was a collard-green hat and the man who wore it had on a heavy wool coat. His big neck was lined with sagging skin and his hair was pewter gray. Mr. Kingsley. A lump formed in her throat.

Mr. Kingsley was the man who monitored the children on Claire's school bus. He was old. When it was cold outside, he stomped his heavy, brown shoes on the metal floor, in rhythm with the trundle of the wheels of the bus. He wore a full length coat and beat his covered hands cross-ways against his chest to keep warm. As if he were a teapot, each blow released a burst of steam from his mouth.

Throughout the long drive to town, Claire watched the man's hat nod over his chest. Once in a while she gazed out the window at the squares of empty fields covered in frost.

The children on the school bus were afraid of Mr. Kingsley. "Keep away from that door, you ragamuffins," he yelled at the boys who wandered out of their seats. They created stories about him. In these stories Kingsley inhabited a dark castle where he dined alone at a massive table, eating the legs and arms of street urchins for dinner. Afterwards, he sat near a blazing fire reading the gospels of Satan and blowing smoke rings with his pipe.

The frosty fields outside the window dissolved into the red brick factories and churches of Bury St. Edmonds.

Claire had never provoked trouble with Mr. Kingsley, but she laughed heartily at the boys who did. Some boys, those with a higher dose of self-confidence knocked off Kingsley's hat when his back was turned, baring his baldness as if it were a vulnerable hole in his armor. Kingsley would whirl around and swat at them while they tossed the dull hat from one seat to another.

Once when his hat fell into Claire's lap, Kingsley snapped it up and scowled into her face. "You're naughty children you are. Some day you'll pay for this. Just you wait."

Claire's bus rolled into the station near Cornhill Square. In her haste to leave before Mr. Kingsley recognized her, Claire dropped her basket in the aisle. She picked up the basket, reached for her mittens that had fallen out and hurried to the door.

"Meet me here at 11:30," her mother said as she set out with the baskets toward the stalls crowding the center of the square. Claire waved and hurried away before Mr. Kingsley exited behind her.

She headed for the shops surrounding the open market. First, Claire walked into the chemist shop. She held a bath cube to her nose, closed her eyes and smelled its fragrance while picturing gardens full of blooming flowers. When she opened her eyes, Mr. Kingsley was walking quickly through the aisles toward her. She dropped the bath cube on the shelf and heard it crumble inside its wrapping. Crowds of people separated them so she skirted around the perfume counter to the nearest door.

It was cold outside. Her breath made puffs of smoke in the air. She swaddled her collar around her neck and looked for an escape. Curry's Book Store was across the street, so she decided to go there to hide and keep warm.

"Could you direct me to the young adult section, sir?" Claire asked the man behind the front counter.

"Yes, darlin'. It's in the very back, behind the dictionaries." A book on the bottom shelf was titled *Old English Folk Tales.* Claire hid in a corner on the floor with her legs crossed and her back hunched against a shelf. She began to read holding the book up to cover her face. Every few minutes she peeked around the edge of the book in case Mr. Kingsley had followed her. In a few minutes Mr. Kingsley strode into the store, his big hands in his pockets, turning his head from side to side. Claire jumped up. Holding her breath and clenching her hands inside her pockets, she slipped behind the shelves of dictionaries and crept along the rows opposite him all the way out of the store.

She wondered if Mr. Kingsley caught her, what he would do. Claire imagined him striding through the fields towards a black castle with her tied up inside a laundry bag flung over his shoulder.

It was only 10:30. Running into the middle of the stalls in the square, she searched for her mother's coat and ocean blue scarf. At every vendor, there were ladies in navy coats bagging fruit and selecting cod, potatoes and turnips. Claire dashed in a zigzag across the square to Moyses Hall, the town museum. Kingsley wouldn't guess she was in there. Children never went to museums by themselves.

Moyses Hall was the largest building surrounding the square, a massive flint and stone house. It was foreboding, like a stone castle belonging to a mean and nasty man. Claire imagined a shelf of chains and screws which Mr. Kingsley used to imprison children that taunted him. Their moans and cries echoed from each suit of armor and glass display case. Soon Claire realized she had escaped Mr. Kingsley and waited in the museum for the hour to pass.

At Purdy's Bakery next to the station her mother was waiting. Two fat market baskets leaned together on the ground next to her feet. Claire ran, anxious to hear the security of her mother's voice. "Hi, Mom. Can we get some sausage rolls?"

"I already bought them from Purdy's. Let's hurry or we'll miss the bus." Claire didn't tell her mother about Mr. Kingsley following her. Her mother didn't know how the children taunted him, and wouldn't like it. They boarded the bus and perched the heavy baskets on their laps.

Boots stomped up the stairs in the back. It sounded just like Mr. Kingsley as he stamped in the cold school bus keeping warm. Claire hunched her shoulders, and hid behind the basket.

A gruff voice bellowed behind her. "At last, I've caught up with you." Mr. Kingsley towered over Claire in the aisle. His eyebrow hairs stuck out of his brow like bent stickpins in an old worn pin cushion. He was so close Claire could see the yellowness of his teeth and the gray hairs inside his nostrils. She shivered as a chill swirled at the base of her neck and crept down into her coat.

"Mr. Kingsley?" Claire's mother said turning from the window, with her eyes opened wide.

Mr. Kingsley thrust his gnarled hand into his oversized pocket. Claire squeezed her eyes shut. There was silence. Cautiously reopening her eyes, Claire saw that Mr. Kingsley was holding her red plaid scarf out to her. "Claire, I saw you leave the bus this morning. You dropped your scarf on your way out," Mr. Kingsley said.

Claire's mouth dropped open. She took the scarf and twisted it self-consciously around her hands. "Thank you."

"Well, I still have more shopping to do before I go home. I better get off this bus before the driver starts up again. See you Monday, Claire."

Her mother said, "Good-bye, Mr. Kingsley."

The picture of Mr. Kingsley's twinkling eyes lingered in Claire's thoughts as she rolled the scarf around her neck.

"What a nice man Mr. Kingsley is," her mother said, "and I'm glad he found your scarf. Keep warm now." Her mother turned to look out the window.

A smile slowly spread across Claire's face. The bus jerked into motion. She was so surprised that Mr. Kingsley only wanted to return her scarf. Maybe he really wasn't the type of man that lived in a dark castle after all.

Stunning When Wet
Aletha Dier

Resplendent you, brilliant and delicious
Striking in your business suit
After a busy day in the dirty city
Driving the long distance to the suburbs
To make this country waif smile

Divine sailor
Tanktop-clad aboard your yacht
Exquisitely muscled body
As gloriously intimidating as the Bay we sail through

But come the swell
Crashing over the leeward side
Catching you by surprise
Me spinning round to see you
Heart stopping in mid-air
Ocean glistening on your smile
Earth's rotation pausing momentarily
Water trickling from your hair
Beautiful always, but stunning when wet!

Hot-tub steam rises through this foggy night
Tamales Bay splashing beneath us
Sumptuous you shining in the vapor mist
I had to pull in closer
Gazing in awe, pupils expanded
To breathlessly kiss your wet lips
Beautiful always, but stunning when wet!

Then sensuous wet splendor
Magnificent you showering
Trillions of delighted droplets
Clamoring to land
On delectable you
I stand enraptured
This chatty child speechless
Oh the extraordinary sight
Of succulent, dripping you
Beautiful always, but stunning when wet!

The Call
Alisa Te Struth

The sirens howled in the night. Their flashing red lights lit the sky with fear. They were in route . . . to me. My parents received a phone call, perhaps the call they have feared since the day I was born. The police and the noise and lights and yelling and panic — I had absolutely no idea I was the cause of it all.

The scene was one in which I would never have imagined being involved. I was at a party with friends and we were drinking alcohol. As an athlete, it wasn't my routine to be at parties, let alone drink. In fact, it was the first and the last time. It was obvious even to the police that my friends and I weren't the normal party crowd.

I had passed out at the party and was discovered thirty minutes later where my friends had left me — lying on the bathroom floor covered from head to toe in a pool of vomit. The paramedics worked as quickly as they could. The alcohol poisoning was severe. My blood alcohol content was .28 percent, enough to kill me. But worse yet, I suffered hypothermia from lying in my own vomit on the cold tiles of the bathroom floor. Had the police and paramedics arrived twenty minutes later, I would have already been dead.

Barely alive, I was rushed in an ambulance to the nearest hospital, as my parents followed the siren's lead. My blood was pumped through with fluids by an IV to rid the veins of alcohol. I was hooked up to an electrocardiograph to measure and watch closely my heart rate of only twenty beats per minute. Three hours later . . .

Bleep, bleep, bleep . . . I awoke to the sound of the electrocardiograph's monotone rhythm. I opened my eyes to the white lights of a hospital, then the faces of my loving parents came into focus. They held my hand and said that everything was going to be all right. I had never felt so twisted inside before. I was scared, relieved, humiliated, grateful, and confused all at once; yet all that I could say was "I'm sorry" over and over again. I can't imagine what I put my mother and father through. "Your mom looked as if she were walking through a dream," a friend told me later.

That night I came closer to dying than I will ever realize. Three teens that year — in the same emergency room — with the same condition as I — didn't make it. No one poured the alcohol down my throat, I did that on my own. Everyone asks why, and I can't tell them. I can't even tell myself.

I see now that drinking is just like playing with fire. It can get out of hand and you can lose control at any time, no matter how careful you are. A lot of parties end in a funeral; this one could have too. I drank. I knew I was doing the wrong thing, but I was naive and didn't listen to my heart. I drank until I lost all judgment — and then I drank some more. The fire lost all control.

I believe now that the reasons for what I did are irrelevant. What's truly important to me is what I did with the lesson that I learned. That thin line that I walked between life and death has taught me a great deal about myself. It was foolish to do what I knew was wrong; I betrayed myself. I will never make that mistake again.

I've gained a new appreciation of life and formed a solid foundation inside. I've discovered how to listen to my conscience and to believe in myself. Honesty and faith hold a new meaning for me. I was ashamed to live knowing that I had betrayed myself and that I had doubted myself, but the new strength that I have discovered within me helped me to rise above the shame. I developed a strong character, high morals, and a sense of confidence and self-esteem that can never be broken again. I owe my life to that night, a life of knowing who I am and how to feel good about myself and my judgments. I see my second chance in life in a new light, but there are memories that will never go away.

I relive that horrifying night with every cry of a screaming siren. I hear their wailing song again and again; bearing a new story of fear, distress, and tears. Their calls go right to my heart and remind me how lucky I am to be alive. And I think about what the next person might learn or lose. Their song was insignificant to me before that night, but now I know . . .

Properties of I: The Mathematicians' Equation of Love

Nicole Burrows

Let X=I. I is logical. I follows theorems. I knows values
are absolute and I acknowledges that unknowns
exist (if and only if) I knows the unknowns are
known. I would like to multiply with U, but can't
because I is negative and if I is negative, the end
product will be negative. I knows this because I
follows logical theorems that are absolute, so I can
not multiply with U even though I would really like
to. I is logical. I follows the theorem that clearly
states "In order for a product to be positive, both
factors must have like signs absolutely, and if one
factor has a sign unlike the other, the product will
be negative absolutely. This is a logical theorem, it
is not up for debate. End of theorem." Alas, U and
I do not have like signs. Logic dictates that the product
of multiplication between U and I will be negative.
I thinks this is too bad, because I really likes U
(despite the unlike sign thing). But I remains logical.
U is irrational (U has always been this way) and
U does not factor well because U is one of those
independent types who does not want to get into
an equation that is too dependent. I understands
this absolutely. I is logical about these things, though
I finds it difficult to stay logical because I thinks U
has great dimensions and I likes U's angles. I
thinks U is pretty acute, but I knows that B thinks
so too. This worries I because B also wants U.

I doesn't like B. B is a radical synthetic who will
multiply with any variable on a horizontal plane
(even with the not so acute ones). B should be
subtracted and divided in two, but that is
hardly a logical solution to this problem (though
it would be absolute). I knows that if U and I multiply
the product will be negative, even though I is very
miserable without U, so what is I to do? Dismiss
logic. I is sick of following theorems. I wants to be
with U (if and only if) U still wants to be with I.

Cocoon

Teresa Brandt

Sister
last night
I heard you calling
I knew you wanted me
ached for me

you took one step towards me
and brought your other foot
to meet the first
so you were balanced
secure before advancing further

I saw you
and extended
my smallest finger
it is my least-used appendage
but vulnerable

my sister, my heart
why are we so shy
afraid to reveal
our pinings
our incomplete characters

oh hush it doesn't matter
I am here
I am willing
be patient
as I emerge from my cocoon.

Himself
Blanche Abrams

At times fiction and reality co-mingle in a "chick-and-egg" type of quandary. The work titled "Himself" contained segments of composite individuals that "real life" individuals claimed were too close to their situations. Although carefully and rationally explained to the individuals, they made it clear that they were not pleased.

Due to legal and other threats the author has elected to omit publication of this winning piece. The author has chosen, along with the publisher and board, to replace the piece with the work beginning on the next page.

Sound Memories
Replacement for "Himself"
Blanche Abrams

The eighty-four years of Grandma's life were being sorted into piles of which relative wanted what. In a far corner they placed the belongings they deemed unworthy of ownership. In that heap were many of her cherished collectibles. I saw the Mr. and Mrs. Santa Claus she placed under her miniature Christmas tree every year. The chipped ceramic windmill salt and pepper shakers her best friend gave her lay in the dust nearby. Then I recognized the multi-colored, wool Indian blanket she always had covering her old Zenith radio.

I turned to my dad, who had lived with her since she became ill. "Dad, where is it? What happened to Grandma's radio?"

"It's outside, on the truck, to go to the dump."

I froze inside. "If no one wants it, can I please have Grandma's radio?"

In an agitated tone, he replied, "Why would you want it? It hasn't worked for years."

Relentlessly I pleaded and he reluctantly removed the other furniture to get at the radio at the far end of the truck. He placed it in my station wagon partially covering it with the Indian rug.

On the way home my mind was racing back to the past faster than the car could carry me forward. I was knocking on her front door at the same time as I did every Saturday. The lace curtain moved slightly as she lifted it aside to peek out at me and smile.

Walking through her foyer I entered a world I so desperately needed. A world where nothing ever changed. The rose-colored Victorian couch with the tufted back and doilies on the arms was in its proper place. Round mahogany end tables with matching lamps completed the ensemble. Oval antique frames presented her only husband, who died many years ago, as well as her five children, who still paid their respects to her often. She never raised her voice to them, nor they to her. And I never smelled liquor on her breath.

An environment so far removed from my own. My parents were in the middle of a divorce. Voices were raised. Bitter words were unleashed and children cried long into the night. My mother searched for strength in the bottom of a bottle. My dad chose to simply walk away. But that was all in the other world, and I was in Grandma's now.

The comfort afforded me by her home was exceeded only by the adventures we shared. And no adventure was complete without food. First Grandma brought in her red Coca Cola tray with a bowl of lime jello that wiggled when she set it down. She would head for the kitchen again and I'd say, "Grandma, can I help you?" "No, I don't want you to see what I made for you," she always replied.

When she returned she proudly placed her white dish loaded with juicy watermelon slices next to the green jello on the red tray. Her last trip produced my favorite treat — golden popped corn oozing with butter. Every Saturday the snacks were exactly the same, but she acted like it was a surprise. And somehow, it was.

Armed with napkins, Grandma sat in her favorite armchair with me at her feet right next to her Zenith radio. Our eyes twinkled with excitement as she turned the dial. The speaker crackled and a booming "Hi Ho Silver!" shattered the silence. I heard hoofbeats and envisioned Silver rearing on his hind legs, shaking his long mane. The Lone Ranger never, ever fell off, and he always wore his knee-high black, leather boots, blue-grey pants, and the shirt with the black crisscross-laced tie, and his gunbelt with the silver bullets. He was exactly the way I had seen him in the comic books. I tried to peer inside the holes in his mask to see the color of his eyes, but I could never get close enough. Tonto was always by his side. Dressed in brown-fringed doeskin and moccasins, with his jet black, neatly plaited braids, he was different than anyone I had ever known. They were the two men in my life who were real heroes. I felt they could never walk out on me.

Grandma and I rode off with them on many a Saturday. We searched for gold and stolen saddlebags and helped find the man with one leg. Tonto needed our aid when he was shot, and we put silver bullets in the Lone Ranger's gun when he injured his arm. Grandma and I lived in the saddle, Kemo Sabe's all the way.

We ended the afternoon sitting on her wooden porch swing sipping lemonade and quietly gazing over her flower garden. I'd like to believe she needed my company as much as I needed hers. Her world was my daily reminder of the need for stability in an unstable family and the need for heroes when parents let you down.

When I die, my children will probably discard the mahogany console filled with dusty tubes and rusty wires. To them it is only an outdated piece of furniture that occupied a silent space in the hallway, but to this day, whenever I walk past Grandma's radio, I could swear I hear the sound of hoofbeats and catch the scent of freshly buttered popcorn.

All I Want For Christmas Is My Writers' Group

Jerry Gervase

Before I joined this gathering
I was far removed from the writing scene.
I thought with just pen and paper
I could write the perfect murder caper.
Or set the publishing world ablaze
with my ability to turn a phrase.
Want to fly a kite? Buy a book on kiting.
Want to learn to write. Buy a book on writing.
Scratch that writing itch, and that itch'll
make me the second Margaret Mitchell.
Soon I had stacks and stacks
of hard cover books and paperbacks
all designed to make me feel
I was as good as Danielle Steele.
I learned the names of every Editor.
I learned an agent can be a predator.
I learned when to use upper or lower case.
I learned when I submitted to include a SASE.
John Gardner taught me plot and point of view.
Hemingway, how to write what is true.
I needed writing information, so to stay abreast
I bought every single back issue of Writer's Digest.
I bought a computer with Word Perfect: Six Oh.
In only one month I could set the margins just so.
I learned every command that a chip could conceive.
I knew how to save and how to retrieve.
I was a leading authority on hyphenation.
People sought my opinion on justification.

I knew line numbering and line height,
knew how to flush left and how to flush right.
The features were beyond my imagination,
it even checked my spelling and handled pagination.
I knew more than any computer nerd knows
and began turning out reams and reams of prose
that I submitted to contests and book anthologies
and were returned with regrets, sincere apologies.
Little by little I comprehended my plight.
I learned everything about writing, except how to write.
It was time to tear down my writing tower of Babel,
So I joined the East Bay Writers' Roundtable.
It was here I met you kind and caring friends,
who used your keen minds and your sharp pens
to show me a world of writing I didn't know -
Here in Rick's living room, on his rear patio.
You used your quiet genius and your talents,
to smooth my rough edges, to bring me some balance.
I know my writing efforts will continue to bloom
with the help of every writer here in this room.
so please accept my thanks, and my good wishes
for a happy, joyous, and very Merry Christmas.
And in 1996 may you get bushels and pecks
of acceptance letters and royalty checks.

About Dan Goldstein
author of
They Could Be Verse

The fun-in-poetry poet, Dan Goldstein, age 85, was born before Arizona and New Mexico ever became States of the Union. Dan has lived through many wars, recessions, boom times, the Great Depression of the 1930's, and he served in the U.S. Coast Guard during World War II. Lately, with everybody concerned about our troubled national economy and the melancholy news from around the world, Dan makes folks laugh with his "belly laugh" poems. No subject is safe from ol' Dan, including politicians and sex. Dan calls the collection of his 140 hilarious poems, "They Could Be Verse."

A wall in Dan's den/workshop is almost covered with framed awards and ribbons that he has won for his fun poems. Dan regularly wins highest awards in poetry and essays categories at the Alameda and San Mateo County Fairs in California and other contests throughout the nation.

The "Across the River" East Bay Writers' Roundtable, based in San Ramon, California, regards Dan as a treasure and an honored guest at the monthly readings and quarterly public readings. Some attend the meetings solely to hear Dan's work, which we strategically save for the "dessert" that ends our literary "feasts."

The Grubby Hubby

Dan Goldstein

A couple was having an intimate date
    On an evening they'd never forget
Beginning with cocktails, then dinner for two,
    In an ardent, intense tête-à-tête.

The restaurant was crowded but they heard no sound,
    So enrapt were they both with their tryst.
Their glasses were filled many times with more wine
    And with each glass of champagne, they kissed.

The evening progressed with more passion and fun,
    As their laughter and ardor increased,
And anyone watching could surely surmise
    What might follow that intimate feast.

But then, just like magic, the man disappeared,
    Just as though he had suddenly flown,
And quite nonchalantly, she sipped at her wine,
    Acting just as though dining alone.

Perplexed at what happened, the waiter bent down
    And discreetly, so others can't hear,
One hand hid his mouth, as he brushed away crumbs,
    And he whispered these words in her ear:

"I hope you're aware, Ma'am, your husband slid down
    And he crawled away, down on the floor."
"You don't understand, sir," she whispered to him,
    "That's my husband, who came in the door."

Which Came First?
Dan Goldstein

Three men were sitting in a bar,
   Engaging in libation,
Enjoying both the liquor and
   Their brilliant conversation.

All three of them were brilliant,
   Each in his own profession,
Their names and fame respected and
   Renowned beyond expression.

Among the three imbibers was
   A surgeon of high station,
Whose miracles of surgery
   Transcend imagination.

Another was an architect
   Whose latest great creation
Was a famous office tower with
   The highest elevation.

And of these three great celebrants,
   One had the nomination
As a leading politician, to
   A top job in the nation.

And as this tippling night progressed,
   Their brainy conversation
Became a competition of
   Profoundest contemplation.

The surgeon, for example, made
   The comment, with discretion,
That his job held distinction as
   The oldest known profession.

For proof, he quoted Genesis,
    With apt elucidation,
That Eve was made from Adam's rib,
    The world's first operation.

All three of them acknowledged this
    With liquid dedication.
They downed a few more drinks to
    Toast his brilliant presentation.

The architect, however, rapped
    The table for attention.
To prove his was the oldest, he
    Expressed this sage contention:

"My learned colleagues must admit
    That God first made Creation.
Before that there was Chaos;
    It's the Bible's revelation.

Architecture is creation, so
    Oblige with your concession:
Since before was only Chaos, mine's
    Indeed, the first profession."

At this, the politician stood,
    Enraged with indignation.
"Since Creation followed Chaos,
    I demand repudiation.

I'll prove that politics came first,
    Though this might well dismay us,
But who the hell do you guys think
    It was who made the CHAOS?"

1995 Writing Contest Judges

Constance Beutel (Adult Fiction) holds an Ed.D. from the University of San Francisco and is the 1995-96 Hewlett Fellow Visiting Scholar at Menlo College, Atherton, CA. She has most recently been published in the field of education for Longman's Publishing, England.

Zoe Francis (Adult Non-Fiction) has a B.S. in journalism from Oklahoma State University. She writes a newspaper column and frequently freelances work for the Tri-Valley Herald and other newspapers in the Alameda Newspaper Group.

Joyce Gunn (Teen Category) received her Masters in Library Science from Rutgers University in New Jersey. She is Branch Manager of the San Ramon Library and was recently involved with writing a revised edition of *Storytelling Art and Technique.*

Kevin Gunn (Teen Category) teaches history at Livermore High School in Livermore, CA, and is the founder of the Knoxville Anonymous Poets' Society. He is a poet, song writer, and winner of awards in the Las Positas Literary Arts Contest.

Bill Harlan (Adult Non-Fiction) is the Director of The Center for Higher Education, a satellite college campus in San Ramon, CA, operated by a consortium of the UC Berkeley Extension, Hayward State University, and Diablo Valley College. He has a B.A. and M.A. in English from UC Berkeley, has been an English instructor at Diablo Valley College since 1964, and has written a textbook, *Probes: An Introduction to Poetry.* His poems, *Christo Rides Again* and *Hiking Into Haleakala* have been honored by the Berkeley Poets and included in the organization's *Ina Coolbrith Anthology.*

Steve Hellman (Adult Fiction) has an M.A. in Creative Writing from San Francisco State University. He teaches a private creative writing workshop and book reading group in San Ramon, and he was a poetry and fiction winner in the 1994 East Bay Writer's contest.

Fred Ostrander (Adult Poetry) worked with *Artists Group of Poets* for many years. He has published in various small press magazines over the years and published one book, *The Hunchback and The Swan*, Woolmer-Brotherson Press, N.Y. He is currently working on a second book, and his work has appeared in the anthologies *Mark in Time* and *Accent on Barlow*. He has given readings in the Bay Area at the Museum of Modern Art and various book stores.

David Wright (Adult Poetry) has been an instructor of English since 1965 in the Chabot-Las Positas College District. He currently teaches creative writing (prose fiction) at Las Positas College and is acting advisor for the school's annual literary anthology. He also created and now oversees the annual Las Positas College Spring Literary Arts Contest, which is open to the community and to college students alike. He has served as chair of the Humanities and Arts Department at Las Positas and was recently appointed by the Mayor of Pleasanton, CA, to the Arts in Public Places Committee. As a poet, his primary interest is Haiku. He spent his 1989-90 sabbatical in Japan to study Haiku and Japanese culture.

Judging Coordinator **Fred Norman** holds a B.A. in Chinese Studies from San Francisco State University and an M.A. in Writing from the University of San Francisco. He has published fiction in *Houdini*, a now-defunct English magazine, and poetry in various anthologies, was a winner in the 1994 East Bay Writers' contest, and currently is the editor of *Griggs Anthology*.

All pieces were submitted to the judges anonymously.

Writing Contest Entries
Postmark Deadline: May 1 of each year

Mail two (2) copies of each submission with enclosed self-addressed stamped envelope and entry fees: $5.00 per poem; $10.00 per short story; $10.00 per non-fiction; $5.00 per teenage submission (teen topics open - High School/18 years and younger). No names on submissions. Name, address, phone, and titles of works on entry form only. $1,300.00 cash awarded. Winning works to be published in annual anthology. No royalties. One-time rights only. Required format: white bond, typed, poetry (40 lines max.); Stories (2,500 words max.); include page numbers.
Mail submissions to: EBWR Writing Contest
c/o Manfit Press
P.O. Box 2390
San Ramon, CA 94583

TITLE:	**CATEGORY:**
	(Poetry, Fiction, Non-Fiction, Teenage)

1. _____

2. _____

3. _____

4. _____

5. _____

6. _____

Entry fee: I enclose $ _____ (+ book shipping see pg. 79)
____ Poem(s) @ $5.00   ____ Short Story @ $10.00
____ Non-Fiction @ $10.00   ____ Teenage @ $5.00
____ 199__ Anthology @ $11.00   ____ '95 + '96 Anth. $17.00

Name:_____
Address:_____
_____ Zip _____
Phone _____

About The Writers' Roundtable

In 1992 the "Across The River" East Bay Writers' Roundtable was founded to serve the needs of writers and members of the publishing industry. The monthly meetings include food, readings, critique, and solid motivation to complete and perfect writing projects.

The group sponsors "Evenings of Literary Enjoyment" featuring local authors and a special theme. The Annual Writing Contest, awards ceremony, and publication of the *Griggs Anthology* complete the list of the group's activities. Group membership is based on the purchase of two anthologies per year. All net proceeds benefit the Writers' Roundtable and selected charities.

Our 1996 Sponsors

To all our donors and sponsors — Thanks!

- **California Design Group**
- **California Western Freight**
- **Color Dot, Inc.**
- **Holliston Mills**
- **Phoenix Color**
- **San Ramon Library**
- **Thomson-Shore Book Printers**
- **Viacom Cable**

The non-profit East Bay Writers' Roundtable is funded by the anthology you are now holding. See back pages for order forms.

To each of you and our sponsors — Thank You!

The International Page
En Français-In Deutsch-En Español

We invite our friends, whether from San Ramon or from any corner of the world, to join us for our monthly meetings, the quarterly readings, or the annual writing contest. If you love writing and literature, join us at the EAST BAY WRITERS' ROUNDTABLE. You will be welcomed by fellow writers.

En Français- Nous invitons nos amis, soit de San Ramon ou de n'importe quel coin du monde de nous rejoindre pour les réunions mensuelles, les soirées de lecture trimestrielles, ou le concours d'écrivains annuel. Si vous aimez l'écriture et la littérature rejoignez-nous à notre EAST BAY WRITERS' ROUNDTABLE, vous serez les bienvenus.

In Deutsch- Wir laden unsere Freunde ein, ob von San Ramon oder irgendwo aus der Welt um unsere monatlichen Treffen, vierteljährlichen Vorlesungen oder die jährlichen Schreibwettbewerbe zu besuchen. Wenn Du das Schreiben und die Literatur liebst, komm zu uns zu dem EAST BAY WRITERS' ROUNDTABLE! Du bist herzlich eingeladen.

En Español- Invitamos a nuestros amigos de San Ramón o de cualquier punto del mundo a unirse a nosotros para las reuniones mensuales, los monentos en la tarde trimestrales o el concurso de escritores anual. Si os gusta escriber o la literatura júntate con nosotros en nuestra EAST BAY WRITERS' ROUNDTABLE. Sereis bienvenidos.

Writer's Missing Link™
Publishing Agent Program

Many writers and authors prefer to focus on the writing part of the business and leave the grunt work, queries, follow-up calls, and rejection to someone else. After many suggestions, we now offer the **WRITER'S MISSING LINK**™ to assist with parts of a writer's life that are often undernourished.

The **WRITER'S MISSING LINK**™ is designed to provide consulting, cataloguing, queries, phone calls, and manuscript mailing. The fee is $75.00 per month* plus agent commission on paid published works. This is not for every writer. It has been designed for those producing publishable material, but who do not have the time, the outlets or the motivation to tackle the murky part of marketing and placement. We do not guarantee placement. We do guarantee wide exposure of well-written, publishable materials.

WRITER'S MISSING LINK™ includes
- consulting on writing style, content, niche
- cataloguing authors' poetry, articles, stories, books
- queries to editors, publishers, specific agents
- phone calls publicizing subscribers' writing
- mailing poetry, stories, articles, manuscripts

Writers will retain copyright ownership and determine the type of rights to be maintained or given with published works. Writers in the program are catalogued and referenced for easy identification of style and types of works of interest to editors and publishers. Agent commissions are 15% of amount paid to authors.

WRITER'S MISSING LINK™ is a service designed and offered by Manfit Press, a division of Griggs Achievement.

* 6 month minimum contract

Special Anthology Orders
Daylight Song + In The Beginning
Two Anthologies for $17.00

Missed last year's Griggs Anthology? Need a "classy" gift for a birthday, holiday, or for someone who loves reading and writing?

For an extra $6.00, you can receive both Daylight Song + In The Beginning. The total is $20.00, which includes $3.00 shipping and handling, for the first two editions of the anthology.

Don't miss out on starting your library chronicling the history of the Writers' Roundtable.

There is only one printing of each anthology.

Be sure you have copies for yourself and others who love writing and literature.

Who knows! Maybe one of these winning writers will be the next Hemingway, Stein, or Fitzgerald!

See order forms at the back of the book.

Manfit Press Books

QUALITY ANGLES
& THE "TANTALUS" COMPLEX
Griggs & Carroll, Edwards, Gorham, Swartz, Warren
Manfit Press - hardcover, 206 pp. ISBN 0-922530-01-7 $25.00

PROFESSIONAL BALANCE
THE CAREERSTYLE APPROACH TO
BALANCED ACHIEVEMENT
Rick Griggs, Manfit Press - hardcover, 209 pp.
ISBN 0-922530-00-9 $25.00

PERSONAL WELLNESS
ACHIEVING BALANCE FOR HEALTHY LIVING
Rick Griggs, Crisp Publications - softcover, 104 pp.
ISBN 1-56052-021-3 $11.00

QUALITY AT WORK
A PERSONAL GUIDE TO
PROFESSIONAL STANDARDS
Diana Bonet & Rick Griggs - Crisp Publications - softcover, 88 pp.
ISBN 0-931961-72-6 $11.00

THE ROAD TO OPTIMISM
CHANGE YOUR LANGUAGE; CHANGE YOUR LIFE
J. Mitchell Perry - Manfit Press - hardcover, 200 pp.
ISBN 0-922530-02-5 $25.00

GRIGGS ANTHOLOGIES
IN THE BEGINNING   ISBN 0-922530-03-3
DAYLIGHT SONG   ISBN 0-922530-04-1
Winners of the Annual Writing Contest - softcovers $11.00 ea.

Also available
Directory of Bay Area Associations
Lorri Fein 510/930-0766

Copy, then mail or fax order form on next page

Book Order Form

For your convenience, please copy this form to order books from Manfit Press. Call 510-866-0793 for quantity discounts. Remember, you can also order these books from your bookstore or ask your librarian about adding Manfit Press titles to the collection.

Name:_____

Address:_____

_____

Phone & Fax _____

Title	**Quantity**	**Price**
QUALITY ANGLES		
PROFESSIONAL BALANCE		
PERSONAL WELLNESS		
ROAD TO OPTIMISM		
QUALITY AT WORK		
IN THE BEGINNING ANTH.		
DAYLIGHT SONG ANTH.		

HARDCOVER SHIPPING- $3 first book, $1.50 per extra title.
SOFTCOVER SHIPPING- $2 first book, $1.00 per extra title.

Total Shipping $_____

Purchase Order # Or Amount Enclosed $_____

CALL IN ORDERS: 510/866-0793
COPY THIS FORM AND MAIL OR FAX TO:
MANFIT PRESS
P.O. Box 2390
San Ramon, CA 94583
Fax 510/866-0827

Text stock: Glatfelter 60 pound offset B6 shade